OUR WORK HERE IS DONE

The Bertie - Bankers - Builders - Bishops and Biffo Years

THE IRISH TIMES

For Henry and Miles. I don't play golf for a living, honest. I do this

Published by: The Irish Times Limited
Design & Layout: Angelo McGrath
Colour reproduction: Irish Times Premedia

© The Irish Times 2011.
© Text and Illustrations Martyn Turner.

ISBN 978-0-90701-135-4

Introduction

One day, many years ago, I was standing in a large exhibition tent in France talking to a small group of French cartoonists. They were explaining to me, slowly (a lot of sign language involved), that a particular cartoon on display was very funny as the words in the caption had two different meanings. "Ah," said I (I'm quite fluent in saying 'Ah' in French. After that I get a bit flustered). "Do any of you know any English?"

"A bit," they said.

"Could you write down a few English words, then," I said.

"D'accord," they said and swiftly scrawled a short list of words.

"That one," I said, "has five different meanings. That one has three and that one six (I was going to say seven if you count a homophone but I had no idea of the French word for homophone. I barely know it in English)."

"It must be very easy," they said, "to be a cartoonist in English."

Well, yes and no.

I grew up in London and in my late teens fled to the peace and quiet of Belfast and, after ten years there, moved to Kildare. In London my family was of the Cockney persuasion and used many words derived from rhyming slang. It was only when I got to my posh secondary school that I found out "the apples" were actually known as stairs in polite company, and that tonsorial delight on the top of my nut wasn't actually my "barnet" but my hair. Who would have thought?

In Belfast I learnt that the correct manner to address someone was "Whataboutye", but I never worked out the correct response. And that "sticking out" means something quite profound. And that they pronounce Belvoir (RTÉ take note) as "Beaver".

Also, I digress, I learnt that Gerry Adams and Martin McGuinness were in the IRA (after 1974 in Martin's case). But apparently they weren't. You could knock me down with a feather, guv, gawd blimey, Luv-a-ducks. Such misinformation. I think I probably mixed with too many West Brits.

"West Brits", there's something I never heard in London. But then I suppose we were East Brits. (We are actually Celts, quite a bit, but that is another book.)

In the Republic, or the Free State or the 26 Counties or Ireland, depending upon who I was talking to, I learnt that you don't call it Eire, except in error, even though it's on the stamps….but then, I guess, you don't go round calling Switzerland "Helvetica" which is on their stamps.

I also learnt that "bold" means "naughty" and not "brave" like it does in England.

And then on trips to America I picked up some of their lingo and have watched sufficient US TV shows subsequently for some of it to stick. I can even do Australian after 6 weeks in the place. I told someone the other day when he took a wrong turn to "chuck a U-eee" and was quite baffled when he drove straight on.

There is also time. Language evolves at a rapid rate of knots these days. At another French cartoon event I was in the company of Yves Michel for three days. He was an editor at a Paris magazine I contribute to (infrequently) that was sponsoring the event. His English was perfect with no trace of accent. As spoken by, well, the English. The explanation was simple. His mother was English and had married a Belgian, a French speaking Belgian. Case closed. But over the three days I noticed that an occasional look of incomprehension would come into his eyes that I couldn't attribute to the fact that I mumble, swallow my words and forget to finish sentences before I move onto the next. Turned out, of course, that his English was actually frozen at 1952, the year his mother left England and, of course, English had moved on apace since then and half the terms and slang I used were post 1952 inventions.

So sometimes trying to find a lingua franca that the majority of readers can understand in my cartoons is difficult. I have to check that I'm speaking Irish English, not cockney or Yankee or whatever. And then I have to check that the reference I may be utilising is understood by a few people outside my immediate family. Years ago, in a politically dry summer, I did a cartoon about introducing music onto Dublin busses. "You have missed the last Victor Sylvester," said a Bus Inspector to a couple in ballroom duds. "But there is a Jackson Five along in five minutes."

"Who are the Jackson Five?" said the editor of The Irish Times.

"A popular beat combo, M'Lud," I replied using the response made famous by a barrister during a trial of a Beatle when the judge asked "Who are the Beatles?". He didn't get that reference either.

The Gay Byrne Presidential cartoon was another case in point. I sit at home and listen to the radio all day and so I am far too familiar with Gay's excruciating radio advert for whatever, some sort of style icon nonsense. But most people don't sit at home listening to the radio. So I broke a golden rule and actually checked with Mr/Mrs/Ms Irish Times before I drew the thing. "Of course we have heard it," said the opinion page editor who sits in a cubby hole in Tara Street waiting patiently by the Batphone on the off chance that I may ring.

And so, to get to the point of this introduction. (About time, isn't this supposed to be a book of cartoons? Ed.) When I drew the cartoon that I have reused as the cover and title of this book I wondered whether anyone would get the reference.

"Our Work Here Is Done" is not a big clue to the fact I'm getting close to retirement. (I'm not. Due to the recession I plan to keep going until shortly before there is white smoke from the crematorium chimney, or until The Irish Times tell me to cease and desist, whichever.) "Our work here is done" was said by the Lone Ranger to his faithful Indian sidekick, Tonto, at the denouement of every half hour black and white tv show that I used to watch round me Nan's gaff after I had seen Leyton Orient lose every Saturday afternoon. I wondered whether it had crossed into the international psyche but in the end, in the absence of any other idea that day, I drew it. And it met with silence, as most of my cartoons do.

But I thought it still fitted the situation to a T and contemplated including it in this year's Irish Times calendar. But I didn't. And then, months later, long after the calendar had gone off to be printed I got an overwhelming public response to the cartoon. Three different people, on three different days, on two different golf courses came over to me and told me that "Our work here is done" was the best cartoon I had done in years.

So I thought, when preparing this book, "why not?". I can always write an introduction and explain it. And I did.

Martyn Turner, October 2011

p.s. Producing a mammoth volume like this is, of course, the work of a highly trained team of professionals whose names would flash by in a nanosecond if this was an episode of Seinfeld. So I would like to thank, slowly, Angelo and Michael for working somewhat beyond the call of duty and to Paul for reading this guff and keeping mum and hardly editing a thing and answering my emails quickly.

Glossary
D'accord = Sacre Bleu, Zut Alors and other things French people rarely say
Nut = head
Knock me down with a feather = somewhat surprised
Gawd Blimey = gosh
Luv-a-ducks = I have no idea what this means but we cockneys say it all the time, apparently
Chuck a U-ee = make an illegal, probably, U-turn
Duds = apparel, both smart and appropriate
Me Nan's gaff = my grandmother's residence
To a T = where does that expression come from?
Guff = rubbish
Mum = stum = silence of a diplomatic nature

2006

Now where was I? My last book ("Up Every Tree - The Bumper Book of Bertie" - Gill and Macmillan - probably remaindered at a book depot near you) ended in 2006 with the funeral of Charles J. Haughey. For once people were permitted to speak ill of the dead.

And of course, joy of joys, we were still allowed to speak ill of the living as well as many world leaders were struggling to keep their political heads above water. And Bertie Ahern wasn't doing too well either. But despite his apparent inexorable slide downhill, the electorate was still, it seemed, willing to give him another chance so long as enough financial incentives were forthcoming. We were all still hoping for a little bit of Celtic Tiger dust.

In the North the Executive went through its pre-birth pangs to give the population the government they deserved - what Harry Barton many years previously called The Queens Own Sinn Féin Republican Loyalist Volunteers (Open to diehards of all persuasions).

On foreign soil, George W. Bush pursued his policy of killing people of all persuasions too and laid the foundation for crippling his own economy to boot. He made the putative Northern Ireland Executive look smart.

July 5 2006

July 6 2006

July 21 2006

August 16 2006

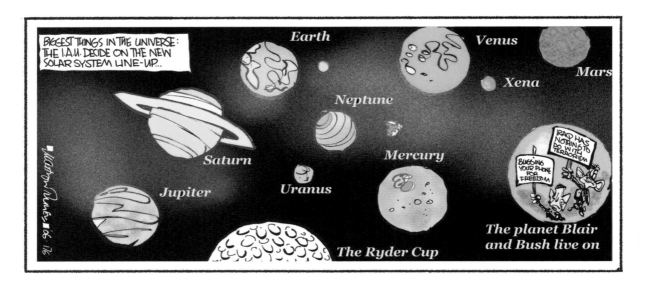

August 19 2006

September 9 2006

September 28 2006

September 30 2006

October 4 2006

October 11 2006

November 1 2006

November 2 2006

November 9 2006

November 17 2006

November 28 2006

November 30 2006

December 7 2006

December 15 2006

2007

2007 started off in an unusual manner when a Fine Gael backbencher attacked his leadership. Gosh, the cad. I bet he feels silly now. It made a pleasant change from the gradual disintegration of Bertie and Biffo.

The aforementioned clung on to power and managed to, sort of, win the election in May with the help of a few PDs and, shock, horror, gasp....the Green Party. Eschewing the chance to let the free market populist parties make some sort of arrangement, the Greens decided trying to save the planet was a better option.

And they tried, for all the thanks they got. But that was back in the days when we thought global warming was the world's number one enemy. We hadn't heard too much about bankers then.

In Bertieworld things went from bad to worse. Mr Ahern suffered amnesia, poor dote, and came up with answers to tribunal questions that wouldn't have even been an option if he had been on "Who Wants To Be a Millionaire". Speaking of which he might already have been a millionaire if only he could remember if he had any bank accounts, where they were and in what currencies they were held. I have some sympathy with him. I once used the excuse, at University, when failing to hand in an essay, that the dog ate it. It was possibly true. So who am I to doubt that he obtained certain monies by winning at the races.

Meanwhile our economic soft landing had the rug, the duvet and all the mattresses pulled from under it.

But just so we appreciate what we have, if we still have any of it, we were reminded that things could be worse. We could be in Zimbabwe or North Korea or in Greater Muslimania working as an illustrator on religious biographies.

January 6 2007

January 9 2007

January 12 2007

February 1 2007

February 6 2007

February 15 2007

February 21 2007

March 3 2007

March 24 2007

March 28 2007

March 29 2007

April 18 2007

April 26 2007

May 2 2007

May 3 2007

May 10 2007

19

May 15 2007

May 24 2007

May 28 2007

May 29 2007

June 12 2007

June 13 2007

June 16 2007

June 21 2007

June 22 2007

July 4 2007

July 5 2007

July 19 2007

July 27 2007

July 28 2007

August 17 2007

September 15 2007

October 4 2007

October 5 2007

October 16 2007

October 17 2007

October 18 2007

November 7 2007

November 9 2007

November 13 2007

November 20 2007

November 23 2007

November 24 2007

November 28 2007

December 5 2007

December 6 2007

December 14 2007

2008

What can you say about the year that had everything, leaving the rest of us with nothing.

Bertie eventually bowed to the inevitable and retired to spend more time with his pensions. He was forced to live in a cupboard in the News of the World, although I believe he has even been thrown out of that now. It would make you weep, if you weren't quietly smirking.

His successors, the Brian and Brian show, tag wrestled with the horrendous economic legacy of Bertie and Charlie (McCreevy) Economics and lost spectacularly. Three falls and a submission in Round One to the tag team of unrepentant failed bankers and irresponsible speculators.

I know a bit about bankers. I went to a 50th reunion of my class at the nondescript English public school that, thanks to a county council scholarship, I attended. I was given a lift to the event by a former classmate.

He said to me, on the trip, "we didn't have much to do with each other at school".

"No," said I, "Why was that?"

"Well," he said, "our form (we didn't have classes, we had forms) was essentially divided into the thickies and the bright boys. I was a thickie," he said, "You were a bright boy."

"Oh," I said, "what happened to the thickies then?"

"Most of them went into banking," he said, "and they have now retired on their bonuses, pensions and early retirement pay offs."

"And what happened to the bright boys?"

"They are like you," he said, "self-employed and still slaving away to earn a crust…."

Abroad Obama appeared on the horizon and inspired the US with his message of "Hope". There is less hope now he has been running the place a few years. Or, to put it another way, they think he is hopeless.

January 5 2008

February 5 2008

February 6 2008

February 9 2008

February 13 2008

February 15 2008

February 20 2008

February 21 2008

41

February 22 2008

February 26 2008

February 27 2008

March 1 2008

March 14 2008

March 22 2008

March 26 2008

March 29 2008

45

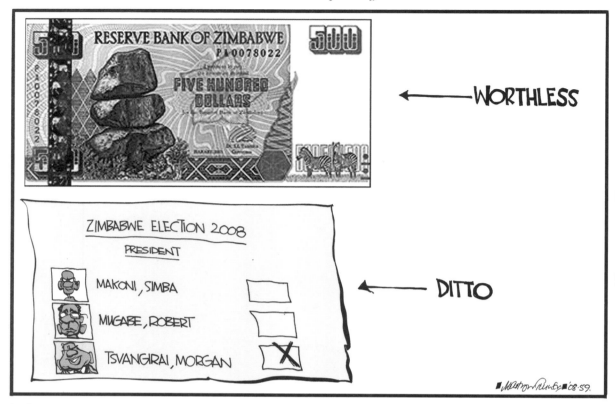

April 1 2008

April 2 2008

April 4 2008

April 12 2008

April 19 2008

May 13 2008

May 24 2008

June 7 2008

June 18 2008

June 21 2008

June 24 2008

July 3 2008

July 10 2008

July 16 2008

July 26 2008

July 30 2008

August 8 2008

September 9 2008

September 19 2008

September 20 2008

September 26 2008

October 3 2008

October 15 2008

October 18 2008

October 24 2008

October 25 2008

November 19 2008

November 29 2008

December 16 2008

December 17 2008

2009

This was the year when all hope of a quiet, normal life went out the window and we woke up each morning to another economic nightmare. We all became experts, a few years too late, in bubbles, booms and busts, bosses, bonuses and bankers. The ba....(that's enough b's; Ed).

Brian and Brian struggled manfully with the complex economics of being totally and utterly broke as only two lawyers could. They paid advisors lots of money. We got NAMA, which includes a scheme to employ bankrupt developers to manage their bankrupt portfolios that, clearly, they couldn't have managed properly in the first place otherwise they wouldn't have gone bankrupt. In a similar vein, we all became beholden to ratings agencies, Standard and Piss Poor, Moody's and the ilk who were otherwise infamous for their AA rating given to Lehman Brothers, shortly before they collapsed and to other American banks so full of toxic financial instruments that they would have needed a gas mask if they had actually inspected their accounts.

If I might digress, and it's my book so I guess I can, I remain constantly bewildered by the need to reward inept incompetents by asking them to have another go. Roy Keane, quoting Albert Einstein, said the definition of madness was to do the same thing over and over again and expect a different result. And yet bankers, ratings agencies, blinkered free market economists, vast teams of accountants and auditors from prestigious but apparently useless companies are still hired to clear up the mess they created in the first place. We still try and operate a laissez faire system of economics that has failed us and will always fail us. John Lanchester in his book "Whoops - Why Everyone Owes Everyone and No One Can Pay" lists some of the changes proposed by various politicians and non-discredited economists to regulate the markets, control the banks and make our economic lives a little fairer and a little less incendiary. He then says he will list the actions taken so far by governments over the page. It is blank.

For a bit of light relief we had another European referendumb...see, I got another 'b' in....and Bertie brought out his autobiography. Only a Bertie autobiography could be written by someone else (isn't that a biography?) and also claim creative artists tax relief for the non-author. And only in Ireland could he be granted it as, clearly, they assumed it was a work of fiction.

January 10 2009

January 16 2009

January 24 2009

January 30 2009

February 3 2009

February 11 2009

February 13 2009

February 24 2009

March 4 2009

March 6 2009

March 7 2009

March 11 2009

March 18 2009

April 14 2009

April 25 2009

April 28 2009

May 1 2009

May 15 2009

May 22 2009

June 8 2009

June 9 2009

July 3 2009

July 11 2009

July 14 2009

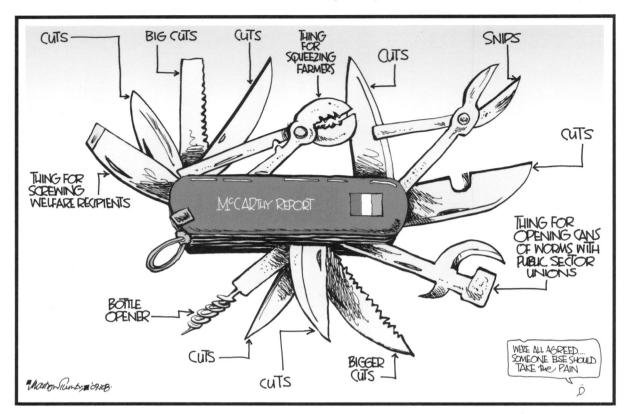

July 17 2009

July 25 2009

July 28 2009

July 29 2009

July 31 2009

August 1 2009

August 5 2009

August 12 2009

August 14 2009

September 22 2009

September 26 2009

September 29 2009

October 3 2009

October 6 2009

October 10 2009

October 21 2009

October 31 2009

November 13 2009

November 24 2009

November 27 2009

83

December 1 2009

December 4 2009

December 9 2009

December 9 2009

2010

The new year in 2010 got us prepared for global warming by freezing our socks off, and then repeated the exercise at the end of the year and the start of the following year. So please stop burning those polluting fossil fuels if you want to stop the icicles and get, er, warmer.

In financial matters we got a new exciting portent of doom.....the PIGS. Portugal, Ireland, Greece and Spain were a threat to the Euro as they were likely to default. Now we all knew, in Ireland, about default as the government had been saying for years that the economic crisis was default of someone else, not them, oh no, someone else, foreign people probably. Of course it is just as likely that the UK (totally broke), the US (also skint and owing quadrillion zillions), Italy and pretty much everywhere else for that matter are also for the financial high jump but PIGSUSAUKI doesn't quite have the same ring about it. It sounds more like a Japanese bank (also likely to default I expect).

For a bit of a change from the dastardly adventures of Bertie and Biffo, the Fianna Fáil gene pool managed to come up with Senator Ivor Callely who was traduced something rotten for claiming a daily season ticket from West Cork to Leinster House when he was, allegedly, living in Clontarf. Was that in the house that was painted by someone who shouldn't have painted it or something? It is really hard to keep up with Ivor Callely. For an innocent abroad (wrong term, that sounds like a bigger expenses claim) he seems most scandal prone.

And the North had a scandal, too, that was nothing to do with sectarianism. It is, apparently, part of the Good Friday Agreement that politicians in Belfast should now behave like politicians everywhere else and get involved in normal politician stuff like expenses fiddling (alleged) and sex scandals (documented). Isn't it great that they have grown up at last.

Haiti got pulverized from something other than its own alleged government. Countries and television crews rushed to its aid until they got bored with the whole thing. Many promises of help were made. Few were realised. But that is because we are all stony broke, except bondholders of course.

January 8 2010

January 9 2010

January 12 2010

January 16 2010

January 26 2010

February 23 2010

February 26 2010

February 27 2010

March 3 2010

March 5 2010

March 19 2010

April 16 2010

April 21 2010

April 23 2010

April 24 2010

April 27 2010

April 30 2010

May 5 2010

May 7 2010

May 8 2010

May 12 2010

May 14 2010

May 15 2010

May 26 2010

May 28 2010

June 25 2010

July 7 2010

July 30 2010

August 4 2010

August 6 2010

August 7 2010

August 11 2010

August 31 2010

September 1 2010

September 11 2010

October 5 2010

October 9 2010

October 29 2010

November 5 2010

November 6 2010

November 9 2010

November 16 2010

November 23 2010

November 24 2010

November 25 2010

November 26 2010

November 27 2010

November 30 2010

December 1 2010

December 4 2010

December 8 2010

December 14 2010

December 22 2010

2011

Ah yes I remember it almost as if it was yesterday, and tomorrow. It was a year of elections, which is a tad ironic as the country is now being run by a troika of self-appointed financiers, known to their families as Mr IMF, Mr ECB and Mr EU.

The general election was hardly a revolution and hardly a revelation. Out went those dastardly populist, conservative Fianna Fáilers and in came those nice populist, conservative Fine Gaelers - propped up as usual by the Labour Party.

Many TDs were ejected by their electorate and forced to spend more time with their pensions. New TDs came in who were independent and didn't wear ties or, indeed and more importantly, have ties.

As if wasting our time and money on a general election wasn't enough we are currently, as I write, engaged in a full blown case of Presidential Election. After Gay Byrne decided he didn't want the job it was open to everybody to run and almost everybody did. With a "Hi Ho, Hi Ho. it's off to the hustings we go" - yes, seven of them.

And, sadly, two of our politicians died. Garret FitzGerald and Brian Lenihan. From two different parties but joined by a rare commodity, integrity. You don't find that often amongst the political classes. Ah, ever the bitter word.

January 19 2011

January 26 2011

January 28 2011

February 4 2011

February 5 2011

February 11 2011

February 16 2011

February 28 2011

March 2 2011

March 5 2011

March 9 2011

March 18 2011

April 8 2011

April 16 2011

May 3 2011

May 10 2011

May 20 2011

May 21 2011

May 24 2011

May 25 2011

July 1 2011

July 6 2011

July 9 2011

July 15 2011

July 20 2011

July 22 2011

August 5 2011

August 16 2011

August 23 2011

August 24 2011

August 12 2011

September 20 2011

September 24 2011

September 27 2011

September 30 2011

October 7 2011

October 8 2011

October 21 2011